JOHN W. SCHAUM PIANO COURSE

Leading to Mastery of the Instrument

ITS OBJECTS

1. **TO TEACH PIANO** in the most natural and the happiest way.

2. **TO PRESENT** technical information accurately and progressively.

3. **NOT TO DEFINE** the scope of Grade I — or Grade II — or any other grades.

4. **NOT TO CONFINE** the intellectual range of the pupil within the 1st year or any other period of time.

5. **BUT TO OFFER** a gradual and progressive pedagogic continuity through a series of Books named Pre-A — A — B — C — D — etc.

6. **LEADING** with the assistance of **THE TEACHER** to eventual mastery of the instrument.

Please particularly note that the division of the Books is not based on a definite interpretation or separation of the various Grades. Neither did Mr. Schaum attempt to define "how much the mind" of a pupil is capable of absorbing within a certain period of time.

Progressive Succession of the "JOHN W. SCHAUM PIANO COURSE"

PRE-A — For the Earliest Beginner

A - "THE RED BOOK" - Grade 1*

B - "THE BLUE BOOK" - Grade 1½

C - "THE PURPLE BOOK" - Grade 2

D - "THE ORANGE BOOK" - Grade 2½

E - "THE VIOLET BOOK" - Grade 3

F - "THE BROWN BOOK" - Grade 4

G - "THE AMBER BOOK" - Pre-Virtuoso

H - "THE GREY BOOK" - Virtuoso

Continue with "AFTER THE H BOOK" in Two Volumes.

*GRADES are listed to serve as an approximate Guide to the Teacher.

B

THE BLUE BOOK

D1384989

E.L. 167

CONTENTS

SIGHT READING DRILLS

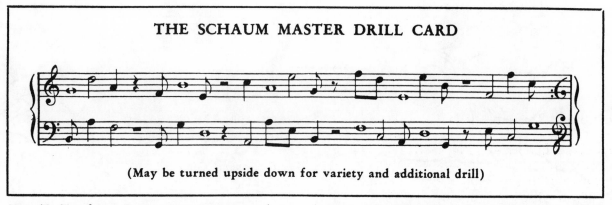

THE SCHAUM MASTER DRILL CARD

(May be turned upside down for variety and additional drill)

Note To Teachers: Devote 5 to 7 minutes of *every* lesson on the following sight reading drills. Your pupils will become excellent readers. Fumbling at the keyboard is mainly due to the pupil's inability to find the notes quickly and accurately. Keep drilling month after month.

Use the Master Card with Each Drill

FIRST DRILL
(Reciting Note and Rest Values)

As the teacher points to the notes and rests on the Master Drill Card, the pupil recites aloud the value of each. No letter names are mentioned, the student simply says, "Whole Note," "Half Note," etc.

SECOND DRILL
(Reciting Treble Letter Names and Note Values)

The pupil recites the names of treble notes as they are pointed out by the teacher on the Master Drill Card. The student says, "G-Whole Note," "D-Half Note," etc.

THIRD DRILL
(Playing Treble Notes on Piano)

The student plays treble notes on piano as they are pointed out on the Drill Card by the teacher. Try hard not to look at hands.

FOURTH DRILL
(Reciting Bass Letter Names and Note Values)

The pupil recites aloud the letter names of bass clef notes as teacher points them out on card. The student says "B-Eighth Note," "A-Quarter Note," etc.

FIFTH DRILL
(Playing Bass Notes on Piano)

As the teacher points out the bass notes on the Drill Card, the pupil plays them on the piano, without looking at hands if possible.

SIXTH DRILL
(Reciting Treble and Bass Letter Names Alternately)

The pupil recites first a treble note, then a bass note, then a treble, then a bass, etc., until all the notes on the Master Drill Card have been named. Letter names only, not note value names.

SEVENTH DRILL
(Playing Treble and Bass Notes Alternately)

The student first plays a treble note, then a bass note, then a treble, then a bass, etc., until all the notes on the card have been played.

EIGHTH DRILL
(Reciting Rhythmic Values: Quarter-Note as a Unit)

Imagine that the time signature on the Drill Card is 4/4. Then let the pupil recite as follows: "Whole Note = Four Counts," "Half Note = Two Counts," etc. No letter names are mentioned.

NINTH DRILL
(Reciting Rhythmic Values: Eighth-Note as a Unit)

Imagine that the time signature on the Drill Card is 6/8. (Whole notes will have to be ignored) The pupil will recite as follows: "Half Note = Four Counts," "Quarter Note = Two Counts," etc. No letter names are mentioned.

TENTH DRILL
(Reciting According to Tonality)

Do Drill No. 6 imagining that the key signature on the Drill Card is one sharp-key of G.

ELEVENTH DRILL
(Playing According to Tonality)

Do Drill No. 7 imagining that the key signature is one sharp, key of G.

TWELFTH DRILL
(Other Tonalities)

Do Drills 6 and 7 in other keys.

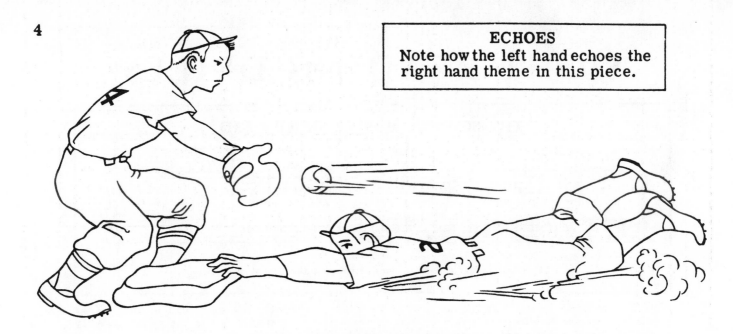

ECHOES
Note how the left hand echoes the right hand theme in this piece.

1. PLAY BALL

Con anima *means* ....

(See Dictionary page 48 for definition)

Copyright 1945 by BELWIN, Inc.
International Copyright Secured

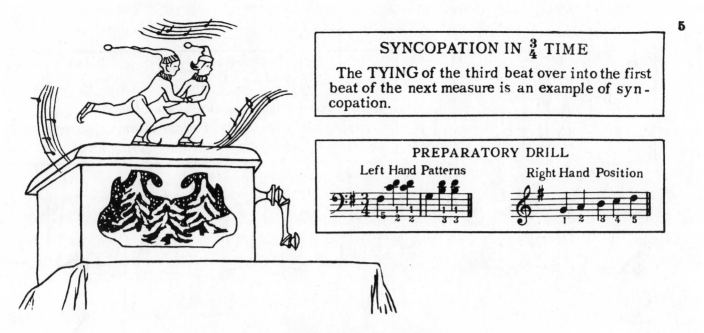

SYNCOPATION IN ¾ TIME

The TYING of the third beat over into the first beat of the next measure is an example of syncopation.

PREPARATORY DRILL

Left Hand Patterns   Right Hand Position

2. MUSIC BOX

Liadow (adapted)

Allegretto *means* ....
(See Dictionary on page 48)

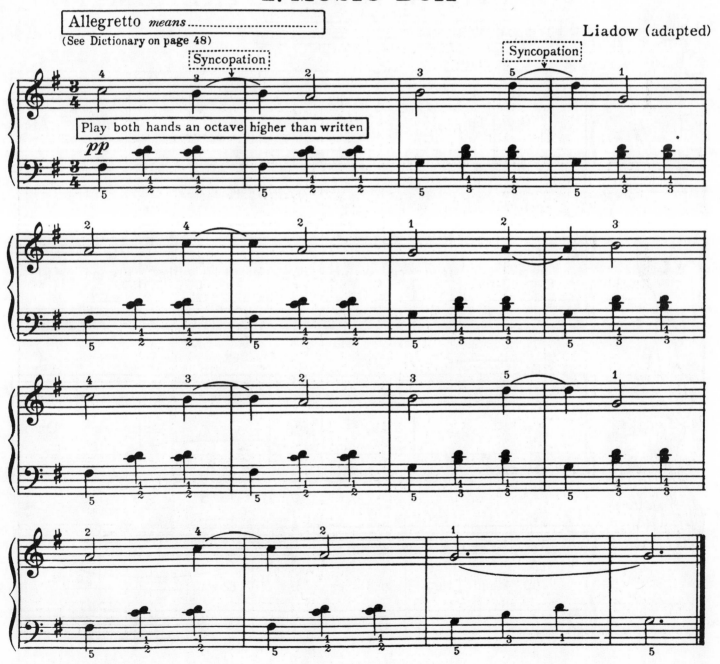

3. STALACTITES AND STALAGMITES

Tempo di Valse *means* ....
(See Dictionary page 48)

mf Sta - lac - - tites, Sta - lag - - mites, Are

Left Hand Melody

formed in caves un - der - neath the ground. Sta -

lac - - tites, Sta - lag - - mites. One's

Left Hand Melody

up and the oth - er is down. _____

HAND POSITION CHART

DIFFERENT KINDS OF ACCENTS
This sign ($\bar{p}$) means loud
This sign ($\overset{>}{p}$) means louder
This sign ($\hat{p}$) means loudest

4. THE COUNTRY FIDDLER

(Key of G - one sharp: F#)

Old English Morris Dance

Allegro *means* ....

L.H. accents

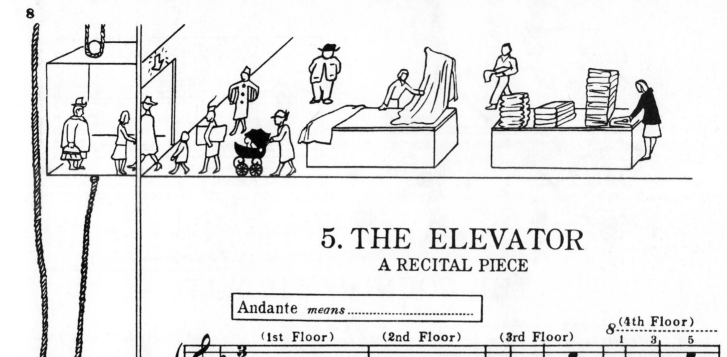

5. THE ELEVATOR
A RECITAL PIECE

A STORY ABOUT BACH

Johann Sebastian Bach is known as the "Father ot Music" because he was the earliest great composer. When Bach was a boy, he wanted to borrow some of his brother's music but his brother refused and hid the music up in the attic. However, Bach found out where it was and late at night he'd go up in the attic and copy the music. After all of Bach's copying, his brother discovered what was going on and burned up all the notes. This did not discourage Bach; he practiced and studied more than ever until he finally became one of our great musicians.

6. THE HARPSICHORD PLAYER

Giocoso means ....

J. S. Bach (1685-1750)

FOLK TUNES are tunes that have no known composer, but have been sung and played by people for generations. This Dutch folk tune has new words that will help you remember a very famous date.

7. THE YEAR 1620

Old Netherlands Folk Song

Andante means ....

The year Six-teen Twen-ty the Pil-grims came o-ver. The good ship May-flow-er brought them 'cross the sea. They land-ed at Ply-mouth Rock, then built up their hou-ses, At har-vest time they start-ed our Thanks-giv-ing Day.

SYNCOPATION IN 4/4 TIME

The TYING of the last part of the first count into the first part of the second count is an example of syncopation.

8. SHORT 'NIN' BREAD

Old Southern Song

Allegro *means* ....

For additional practice in syncopation, it is recommended that the student study DONALD THE DINOSAUR by John W. Schaum.

E. L. 167

In Mozart's Opera "The Magic Flute" there is a funny man (Papageno) whose flute music makes everyone want to dance. Even burly, fierce soldiers who come to catch Papageno can't touch him because they are all tired out from dancing.

Mozart, the composer, was the boy-wonder who traveled all over Europe, before he was seven, entertaining the royal families with his violin and piano playing.

9. MAGIC FLUTE

Mozart (adapted)

Allegretto *means* ....

For another splendid Mozart composition, the student may learn OVERTURE TO MARRIAGE OF FIGARO arranged by John W. Schaum.

E L 167

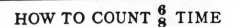

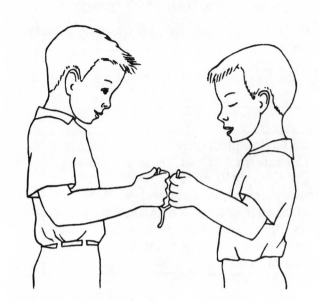

10. THE WISHBONE

HOW TO ACCENT $\frac{6}{8}$ TIME
Play the first and fourth counts louder, as follows:

| 1 2 3 4 5 6 | 1 2 3 4 5 6 |

The Campbells Are Coming. Don't mistake this for "The Camels are Coming." The Campbells were a powerful and wily family (clan) in Scotland who warred with other groups. The Campbells generally won, and their prestige and power grew until their song became the National Song of Scotland.

11. THE CAMPBELLS ARE COMING

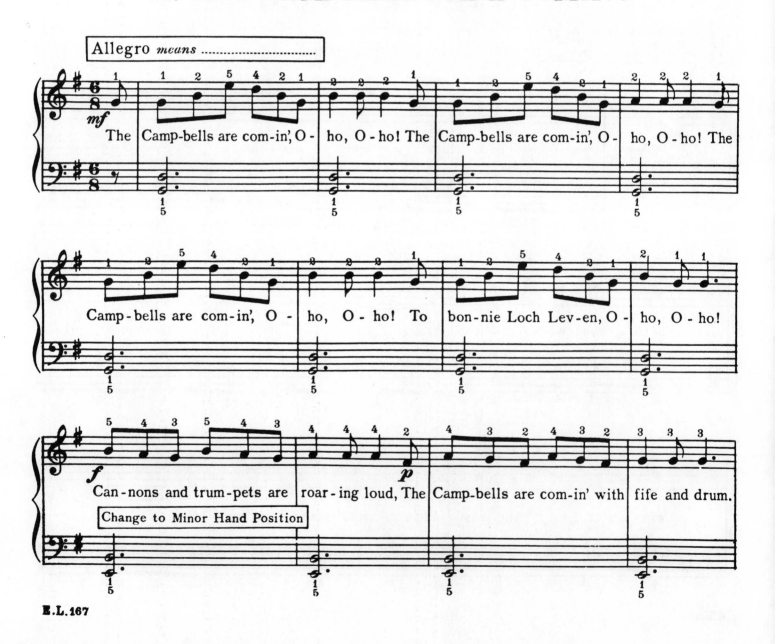

Shoot-ing and shout-ing in dus - ty clouds, The Camp-bells are fight-ing to o -ver come. To

bon-nie Loch Lev-en, O - ho, O-ho! The Camp-bells are com-in', O - ho, O-ho! The

Change back to 1st Hand Position

Camp-bells are com-in', O - ho, O-ho! To bon-nie Loch Lev-en, O - ho, O-ho!

E.L. 167

Schubert wrote this stirring march original-
ly as a piano duet, but it was so gay and brilliant
that it was dedicated to the Army of Imperial
Grenadiers.

Franz Schubert (the kind-looking composer
with thick glasses) wrote over **600** songs besides
symphonies and sonatas, but he was so poor that
he often paid his bills with his original composi-
tions.

12. THE DRESS PARADE
(MARCHE MILITAIRE)

Con brio *means* ....

Schubert (adapted)

Supplementary Sheet Music Hints

FLYING G-MEN MARCH (Gallini) arranged by John W. Schaum.
RIDE RANGER RIDE (Offenbach) arranged by John W. Schaum.

E. L. 167

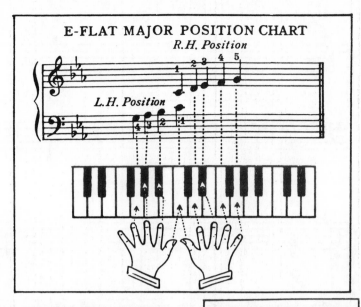

13. LITTLE BROWN BUG
(Key of E♭ - Three flats: B♭, E♭ and A♭)

KEEP UP THE SIGHT
READING DRILLS
especially nos. 6 and 7

THE HOLD
This sign 𝄐 is called a Hold and prolongs the value of a note.

THE DICTIONARY HABIT
There is a music dictionary on page 48. It contains all musical terms used in this book plus many others that you are likely to find in your supplementary sheet music.

Get the dictionary habit. Look up all word meanings. Recent research in intelligence tests shows that persons who rank high in intelligence invariably have large vocabularies.

14. SAILING

Old Song of the Sea

HOW ARE YOU PRACTICING?

Can you play five of your pieces without a mistake? Here is a story: A pupil came to Leschetizsky (a great piano teacher) and said, "Maestro, I practice and practice, yet I never play perfectly!" Then Leschetizsky took ten buttons from a little box. "Here," he said, "place a button on the piano each time that you play one page perfectly. If you make one mistake, you must put all the butttons back in the box and start over. Then you will learn to play carefully."

That was advice for a concert pianist, but you can get your own buttons and play each line of music five times perfectly each day. Remember, only *perfect practice makes perfect playing*.

15. THE CLOTHES LINE WALTZ

Tempo di Valse *means* ....

Bass Clef

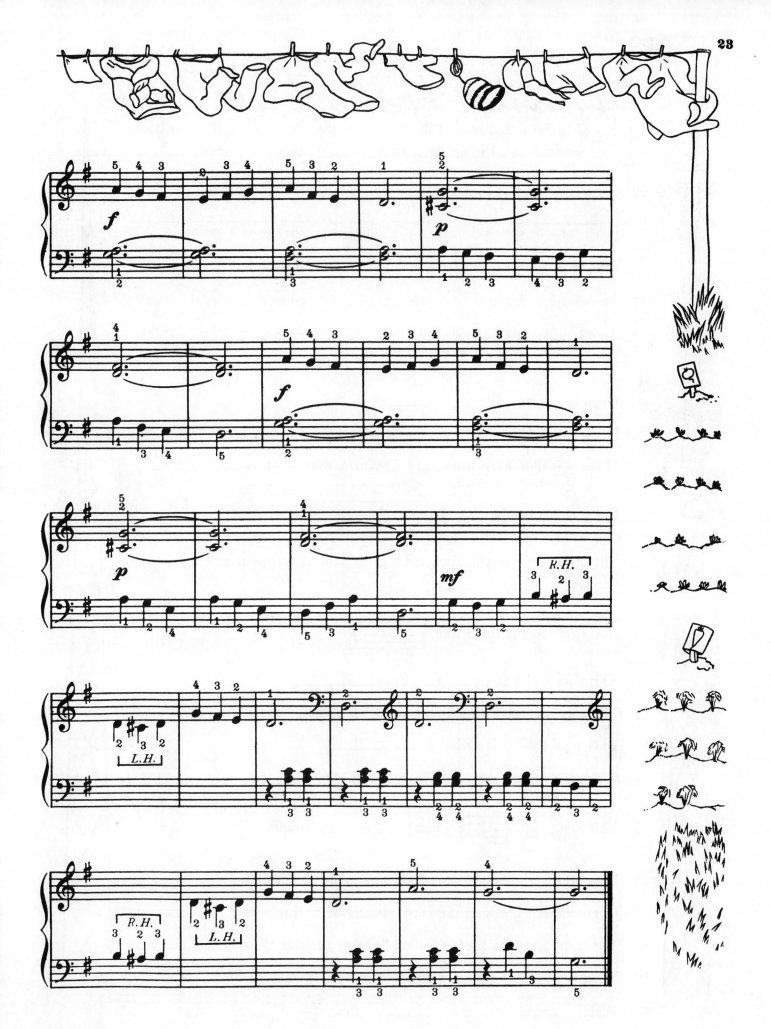

Schaum Piano Quiz No. 1

Before taking this test, the pupil should review the previous pages of the book.

Directions: Fill in the blanks with the correct answers:

Date_____   Grade Marked_____

_____   _____
(Signature of Student)   (Signature of Teacher)

1. In 3/4 time, this note ♩ gets _____ counts.

2. In 6/8 time, this note ♩ gets _____ counts.

3. In 4/4 time, this note ♩ gets _____ counts.

4. This sign (>) is called an _____ mark.

5. Draw a quarter note. _____

6. Draw a note that would get 2 counts in 4/4 time. _____

7. If there is one sharp in the key signature, that sharp is _____.

8. Put a sharp on the second space.

9. The boy musician who attracted a great deal of attention among Royalty
   was _____.

10. Put a flat on the third line.

11. This sign (∧) in music, tells us to _____.

12. The musician who wrote many hundreds of songs was _____.

13. This sign (⌒•) is called a _____.

14. One piece that I've played that is a Folk Tune is _____.

15. This rest _____ gets _____ counts.

16. Draw the note that gets the same time value as this rest (ξ). _____

17. Draw the rest that gets the same time value as this note (♪). _____

18. The composer who is often called "Father of Music" is _____.

19. When I see *pp* in music, I will play _____.

20. Waltzes are written in _____ time.

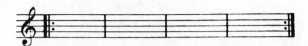
16. MONKEY SEES! MONKEY DOES!

(Legato Thirds)

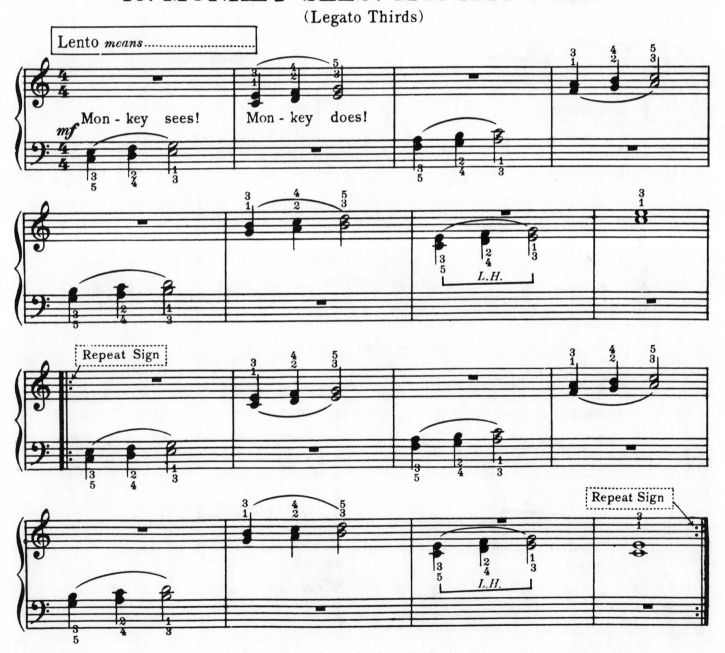

E.L. 167

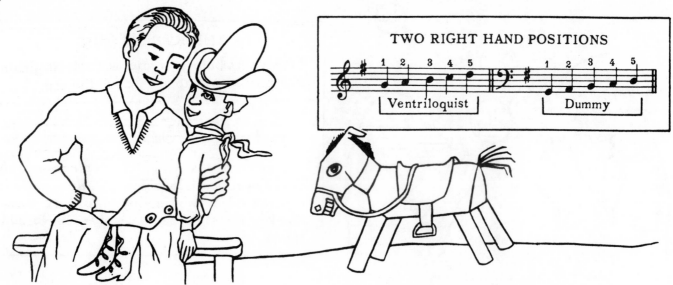

TWO RIGHT HAND POSITIONS

Ventriloquist

Dummy

17. THE VENTRILOQUIST AND HIS DUMMY
(STUDY IN CROSS HANDS)

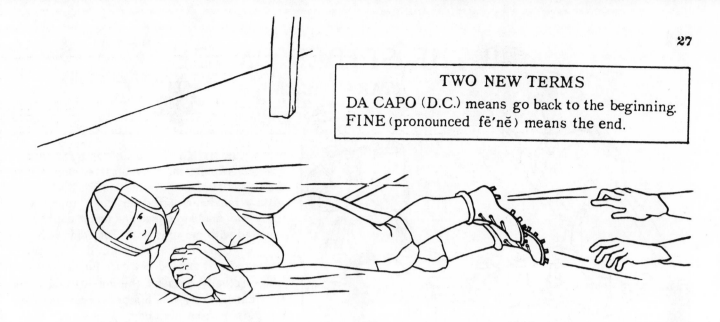

18. HERE WE GO FOR A TOUCH-DOWN
(CHANGING KEYS)

E.L. 167

19. THE SPIDER DANCE
(TARANTELLE)

Tony an Italian boy was bitten by the deadly poisonous spider, the tarantula. He would surely die unless Mother did something quickly. The village musician played her magic tune while Tony was made to dance and dance until he fell covered with perspiration. Tony didn't die, and the music and dance (now called Tarantelle) came to be regarded as a cure for the tarantula bite. Actually, it wasn't the music or dancing that cured Tony, but his perspiration drove the poison from his body.

Vivace *means* ....

SIXTEENTH NOTES

Two sixteenth notes (♫) make an eighth note (♪). Notice the sixteenth notes each time the word "Chinese" occurs in the piece.

20. WUN LONG PAN
(FAMOUS CHINESE DETECTIVE)

Moderato

16th Notes

Wun Long Pan, Is fam - ous Chi - nese De - tec - tive.

mf

Wun Long Pan, He gives the crooks a chase.

mp

Wun Long Pan, Is fam - ous Chi - nese De - tec - tive.

mf

Wun Long Pan, He al - ways solves the case.

mp

Observe the phrase releases carefully. It will portray the snipping of the barber's scissors.

21. THE BARBER
(TWO NOTE SLURS)

Le Couppey (arranged)

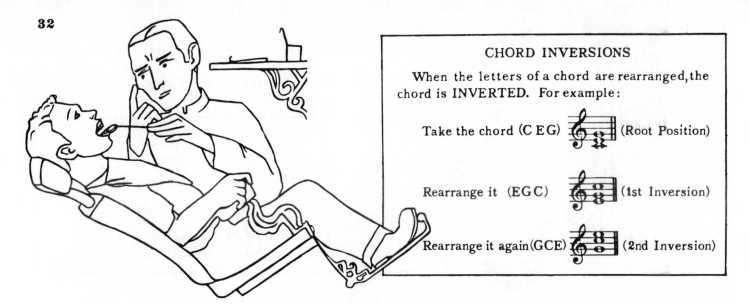

22. THE DENTIST

E.L. 167

ROBERT SCHUMANN liked writing stories almost as much as writing music. Here are a few rules from his book "Rules For Young Musicians."

1. Play in time! The playing of many virtuosos is like the gait of a drunkard. Make not such your models.

2. Strive to play easy pieces well and beautifully; it is better than to render harder pieces only indifferently well.

3. Always play as if a master heard you.

4. Dragging and hurrying are equally great faults.

24. STRANGE LANDS
(PEDAL STUDY)

Robert Schumann (adapted)

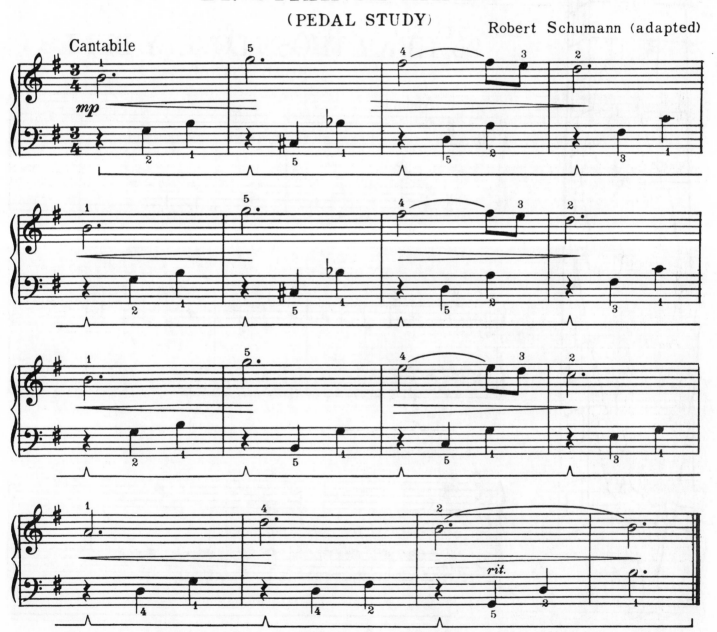

At this point, the student can learn KNIGHT RUPERT by Robert Schumann, especially arranged by John W. Schaum.

E.L. 167

25. HEAR THOSE LOVELY BELLS
(CHORD STUDY)

A very playable arrangement of Schubert's **AVE MARIA** by John W. Schaum is appropriate here.

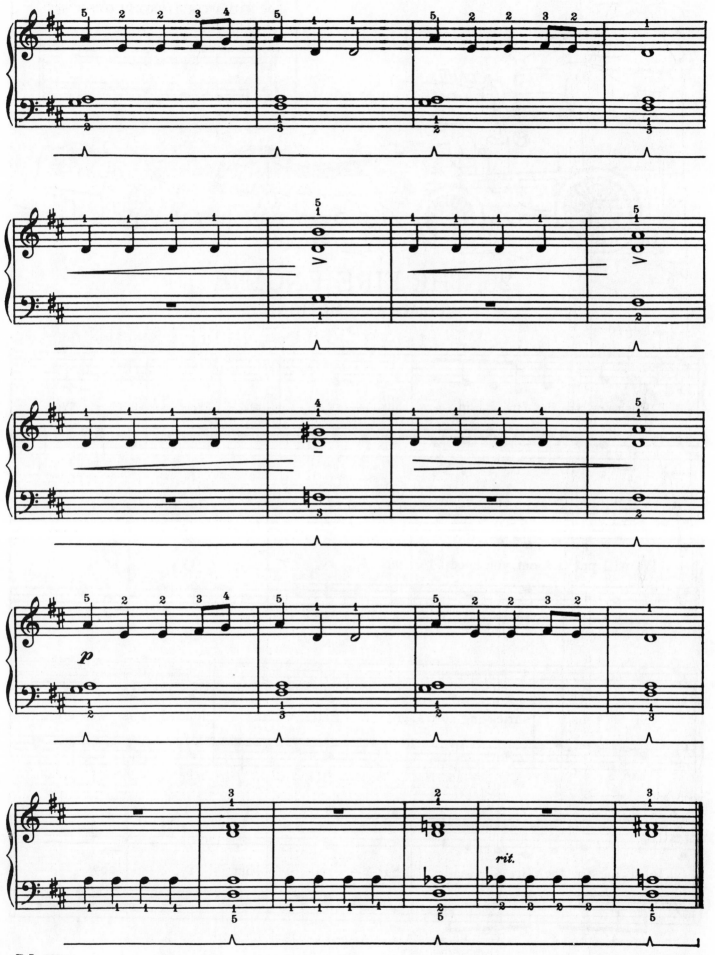

26. THE FIRE ENGINE
(CONTRARY MOTION)

Allegro

Rush-ing to the fire   in a   hur - ry,   hur - ry,   hur - ry.

We will put it   out; you need-n't   wor - ry,   wor - ry   now.

Si - rens   shriek-ing as we go,   Bells clang   loud-ly as we go.

Rush-ing to the fire   in a   hur - ry,   hur - ry,   now.

E.L. 167

27. A FINE STATE OF AFFAIRS
(WRIST STACCATO STUDY)

Duvernoy (adapted)

CAVALRY TROT by Anton Rubinstein arranged by John W. Schaum is an excellent wrist staccato study.

E.L. 167

E MAJOR POSITION CHART

28. THE TELEGRAPH OPERATOR

(Key of E Major – Four sharps: F♯, C♯, G♯ and D♯)

29. OVER THE HURDLES

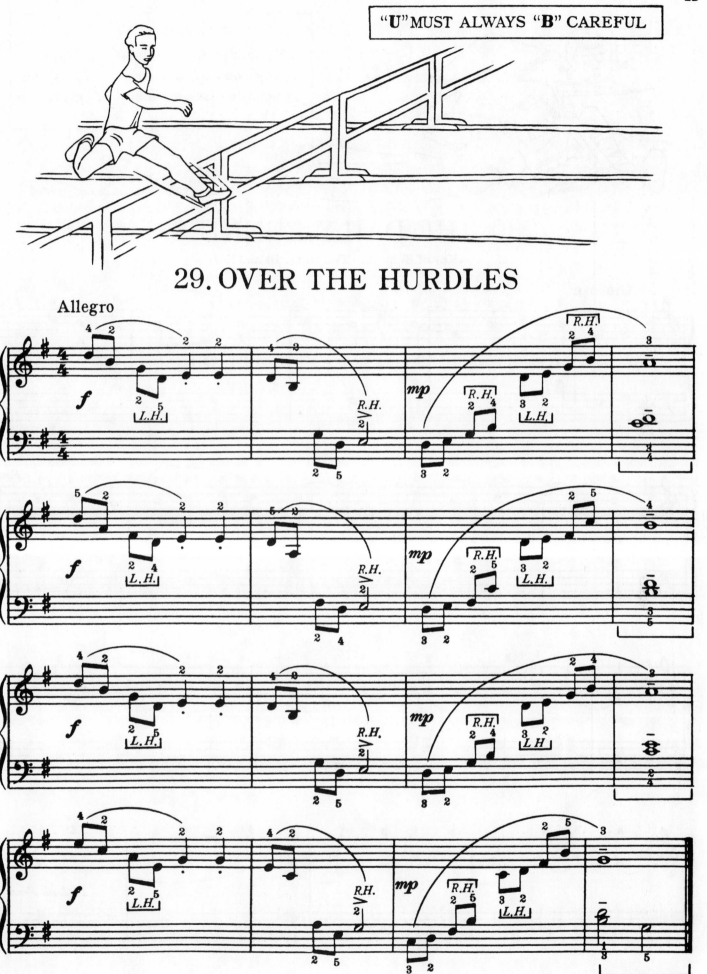

30. THE DAILY FUNNIES

(Key of B♭ Major - Two flats: B♭ and E♭)

CHROMATIC PASSAGES

L.H. Chord Patterns

31. PUTTING SALT ON A BIRD'S TAIL
(or How Not To Catch a Bird)

Con moto

32. ON THE LEVEE
RECITAL PIECE

Old American Song

Moderato

Plink, plink, plink, plink, | Hear the ban-jos strum-min', | Plink, plink, plink, plink,

Roun' the cab-in door; | Plink, plink, plink, plink, | Hear the feet a drum-min',

Sheet Music Suggestion
AT A DARKY CAMP MEETING arranged by John W. Schaum.

E. L. 167

Schaum Piano Quiz No-2

Before taking this test, the pupil should review the previous pages of the book.
Directions: Fill in the blanks with the correct answers:

Date_____ Grade Marked_____

_____ _____
(Signature of Student) (Signature of Teacher)

1. When I see this sign (*f*), I will play _____.

2. If there are two sharps in the key signature, they are _____ and _____.

3. The sign that means "go back to the beginning and play to the end" is _____.

4. In 4/4 time, the note that gets one count looks like this _____.

5. In 6/8 time, the note that gets one count looks like this _____.

6. Draw two 16th notes _____.

7. The connecting line 🎵 is called a _____.

8. Draw a rest that gets one count in 3/4 time _____.

9. Draw a note that gets two counts in 2/4 time _____.

10. In 3/8 time, I will count _____ to each measure.

11. When you rearrange the letters of a chord it is called _____.

12. Another name for the Spider Dance is _____.

13. This sign (⌐⌐⌐) is a _____ mark.

14. The composer who wrote "Strange Lands" was _____.

15. If there are two flats in the signature of a piece, they are _____ and _____.

16. These signs (▦) are called _____ signs.

17. Another name for the end of a piece is _____.

18. The connecting line (🎵) is called a _____.

19. L.H. in music stands for _____.

20. What do we emphasize in a piece?
(melody or accompaniment) _____.